RISING ★ STARS
ASSESSMENT

Grammar, Punctuation and Spelling

Progress Tests

Year

3

Marie Lallaway

Series Advisors: Cornwall Learning

Rising Stars UK Ltd, 7 Hatchers Mews, Bermondsey Street, London SE1 3GS

www.risingstars-uk.com

Published 2014
Reprinted 2014 (five times)

Text, design and layout © Rising Stars UK Ltd 2014

All facts are correct at time of going to press.

The right of Marie Lallaway to be identified as the author of this work has been asserted by her in accordance with the Copyright, Design and Patents Act 1998.

Author: Marie Lallaway
Educational Consultant: Sara Moult, Cornwall Learning
Series Editor: Maddy Barnes
Accessibility reviewer: Vivien Kilburn
Editorial: Sarah Davies, Sparks Publishing and Dodi Beardshaw
Design: Andy Wilson for Green Desert Ltd
Cover design: Burville-Riley Partnership

Rising Stars is grateful to the following people and schools who contributed to the development of these materials:
Plumcroft Primary School, London; St Helens Teaching Schools Alliance; St Nicholas CE Primary School, Chislehurst;
St Margaret's CE Primary School, Heywood, Rochdale; St Peters Primary School, Burnley; Tennyson Road Primary School, Luton

British Library Cataloguing in Publication Data.
A CIP record for this book is available from the British Library.
ISBN: 978 1 78339 132 5

Printed by Ashford Colour Press

Contents

Introduction

Why use Rising Stars Assessment Progress Tests?

The *Rising Stars Assessment Grammar, Punctuation and Spelling Progress Tests* have been developed to support teachers assess the progress their pupils are making against the grammar, spelling, vocabulary and punctuation requirements of the 2014 National Curriculum Programme of Study for English in Years 2 to 6. Separate progress tests are available to cover the requirements for reading. For Year 1 there is a single set of progress tests for English. All *Rising Stars Assessment Progress Tests* are designed to support effective classroom assessment and are easy to use and mark.

The *Rising Stars Assessment Grammar, Punctuation and Spelling Progress Tests* include separate half-termly tests for spelling and for grammar, punctuation and vocabulary. All the tests have been:

- written by primary English assessment specialists
- reviewed by primary English curriculum and assessment experts.

How do the tests track progress?

The results data from the tests can be used to track progress. They show whether pupils are making the expected progress for their year, more than expected progress or less than expected progress. This data can then be used alongside other evidence to enable effective planning of future teaching and learning, for reporting to parents and as evidence for Ofsted inspections. If teachers are using the CD-ROM version of the tests, the results data can be keyed into the Progress Tracker (see pages 6–7 for more information) which automatically shows the progress of individual pupils against the Programme of Study and the results for all pupils by question and test. Data can also be exported into the school's management information system (MIS).

About the Grammar, Punctuation and Vocabulary and Spelling Progress Tests

The tests are written to match the requirements of the Programme of Study for the 2014 National Curriculum including the Appendices for English. For each half term there is a grammar punctuation and vocabulary test and a separate spelling test. The number of marks for each test is as follows:

	Year 2	Year 3	Year 4	Year 5	Year 6
Grammar, punctuation and vocabulary, of which:	10	20	20	20	20
• Grammar	5	10	10	10	10
• Punctuation	3	6	6	6	6
• Vocabulary	2	4	4	4	4
Spelling	20	20	20	20	20

The style of the tests mirrors that of the tests pupils will take at the end of Key Stage 2. Spellings are assessed using contextualised sentences. Questions in the grammar, punctuation and vocabulary tests use the cognitive domains derived from Bloom's taxonomy: knowledge, comprehension, application, analysis, synthesis and evaluation.

Test demand

Test demand increases both within tests and across the year, which means that tests at the beginning of the year are easier than those at the end of the year. Difficulty is also built into each test with questions increasing in difficulty as pupils work their way through. In the grammar, punctuation and vocabulary tests, questions become more demanding in terms of response type, progressing from simple 'tick/circle' the correct response to requiring pupils to give an explanation of an answer. The questions for each of grammar, punctuation and vocabulary are distributed throughout each test rather than in blocks within a test.

Tracking progress

The marks pupils score in the tests can be used to track how they are progressing against the expected outcomes for their year group. The marks for each test have been split into three progress zones:

- less than expected progress
- expected progress
- more than expected progress.

The zones for each year group are as follows:

		Zone mark range		
		Less than expected progress	**Expected progress**	**More than expected progress**
Year 2	GPV	0–5	6–8	9–10
	spelling	0–11	12–16	17–20
Year 3		0–11	12–16	17–20
Year 4		0–11	12–16	17–20
Year 5		0–11	12–16	17–20
Year 6		0–11	12–16	17–20

The table gives the mark ranges for the progress zones for each test which you can use to see how well each pupil is doing in each test. If pupils are making the expected progress for their year they will be consistently scoring marks in the middle zone of marks in the tests. The higher the mark in the zone, the more secure you can be that they are making expected progress.

How to use the Grammar, Punctuation and Vocabulary and Spelling Progress Tests

Preparation and timings

1 Make enough copies of the test(s) for each pupil to have their own copy. Note that the spelling test script containing the instructions for teachers is provided separately.
2 Hand out the papers and ensure pupils are seated appropriately so that they can't see each other's papers.
3 Pupils will need pens or pencils and erasers. Encourage pupils to cross out answers rather than rub them out.
4 There are no time limits for the tests but normal practice is to allow a minute per mark for written tests. Help with reading may be given using the same rules as when providing a reader with the DfE KS2 tests.

Supporting pupils during the tests

Before the test, explain to the pupils that the test is an opportunity to show what they know, understand and can do. They should try to answer all the questions but should not worry if there are some they can't do.

Many pupils will be able to work independently in the tests, with minimal support from the teacher or a teaching assistant. However, pupils should be encouraged to 'have a go' at a question, or to move on to a fresh question if they appear to be stuck, to ensure that no pupil becomes distressed.

It is important that pupils receive appropriate support, but are not unfairly advantaged or disadvantaged. Throughout the tests, therefore, the teacher may read, explain or sign to a pupil any parts of the test that include instructions, for example by demonstrating how to circle an answer.

With younger age groups you may also consider using the version of the test on the CD-ROM and projecting it on to a whiteboard to support a whole class or group to take the tests. You may choose to refer to the words on the whiteboard and read them aloud so that pupils can follow them on the screen and on their own test paper, and then write their answers on their papers individually.

Marking the tests

Use the detailed mark scheme and your professional judgement to award marks. Do not award half marks.

It is useful to use peer marking of test questions from time to time. Pupils should exchange test sheets and mark them as you read out the question and answer. You will need to check that pupils are marking accurately. This approach also provides an opportunity to recap on any questions that pupils found difficult to answer.

Feeding back to pupils

Once the test has been marked, use a five-minute feedback session with the pupils to help them review their answers. Wherever possible pupils should be encouraged to make their own corrections as in this way they will become more aware of their own strengths and weaknesses. Agree with each pupil what they did well in the test and what the targets are for them to improve. A template Pupil progress sheet is provided on page 8 for this purpose.

Using the Progress Tracker

The table on page 5 gives the mark ranges for the progress zones for each test, which you can use to see how well each pupil is doing in each test. If pupils are making the expected progress for their year they will be consistently scoring marks in the middle zone of marks in the tests. The higher the mark in the zone, the more secure you can be that they are making expected progress.

The CD-ROM* version of *Grammar, Punctuation and Spelling Progress Tests* includes an interactive Progress Tracker, which allows you to enter the marks for each question for each test by pupil. This then automatically shows you which zone the pupil is in and also the zone distribution for the class so that you can track the progress of individual pupils and the whole class.

*If you have the book version only of *Grammar, Punctuation and Spelling Progress Tests*, the Progress Tracker can be downloaded from bit.ly/progtracker

The Progress Tracker also enables you to review the marks for each question so that you can identify areas where some or all pupils may need further support and areas where some or all pupils are ready to be stretched further.

If required, data from the tests can be exported into the school's management information system (MIS) so that it can be used alongside other data in whole school monitoring including the monitoring of specific groups of pupils, such as Pupil Premium.

Full details about the Progress Tracker are provided on the CD-ROM.

Pupil progress sheet

Name: _____ Class: _____ Date: _____

Test name: _____ Test number: _____ My mark: _____

What I did well in the test:

_____

_____

_____

What I need to do to improve:

1. _____

2. _____

3. _____

✂ —

Pupil progress sheet

Name: _____ Class: _____ Date: _____

Test name: _____ Test number: _____ My mark: _____

What I did well in the test:

_____

_____

_____

What I need to do to improve:

1. _____

2. _____

3. _____

Year 3   *Autumn test 1*

Name:	Class:	Date:

1   Apples _____ bananas are my favourite fruits.

Circle the word which completes the sentence.

and   because   if   so

G
1 mark

---

2   Tick **one** box to show which letter should be a capital letter.

☐   ☐   ☐☐

please bring your swimming kit tomorrow.

P
1 mark

---

3   Tick **one** box to show the sentence that is a command.

Where are you going?   ☐   Go to bed.   ☐

Help!   ☐   The fox chased the chickens.   ☐

G
1 mark

---

4   Circle the **two** words which are plural nouns.

apple   peaches   orange   bananas

V
1 mark

/ 4

Total for this page

5 kind + ness = kindness

Circle the **two** words which make a new word when you add **-ness**.

dark   moon   sad   sky

V
1 mark

---

6 Tick the box to show which letter should be a capital letter.

☐   ☐ ☐ ☐
↓   ↓ ↓ ↓
I know that ben likes tennis.

P
1 mark

---

7 Circle the missing word to complete this sentence.

Tom calls his cat Tiger _____ it has stripes.

and   because   but   if

G
1 mark

---

8 Write the correct word into this sentence.

Sam screamed when the monster _____ through the window.

look   looked   looks   looking

G
1 mark

/ 4
Total for this page

9 I don't like milk _____ I do like water.

Circle the word which completes the sentence.

   and   but   because   when

G
1 mark

---

10 Tick **two** boxes to show where the commas should go.

☐   ☐   ☐   ☐

Sanji's favourite animals are lions tigers bears and elephants.

P
1 mark

---

11 Draw lines to show which word ('a' or 'an') goes with the nouns.
One has been done for you.

   ant

   flower

a

an   insect

   tree

V
1 mark

---

12 Tick **two** boxes to show where the speech marks (inverted commas) should go.

☐   ☐ ☐ ☐

You are my best friend, said Noor.

P
1 mark

/ 4
Total for this page

13 Write a correct conjunction to complete this sentence.

You can come to the park with us _____ you like.

G
1 mark

14 Write **one** adjective to complete this sentence:

Ali and Ben both have _____ bicycles.

G
1 mark

15 Write a question which will get the answer 'Yes.'

_____?

G
1 mark

16 Circle the correct word to complete this sentence.

Josh can run fast but Aaliyah can run (faster / fastest) than Josh.

G
1 mark

/ 4
Total for this page

17 Complete the words in these sentences.

My sister is quite forget_____.

She is also a very joy_____ person.

V

1 mark

---

18 This sentence has two mistakes. Make **two** changes and copy out the sentence correctly.

I likes making Bread on Saturdays.

_____

G

1 mark

---

19 Why is an apostrophe used in these words?

can't   don't

Apostrophes are used in these words because _____

_____.

P

1 mark

---

20 Explain why '**!**' is used at the end of this sentence.

That's terrible!

! is used _____.

P

1 mark

/ 20

Total for this test

Year 3   Autumn spelling test 1: *Teacher's script*

This test should take approximately 15 minutes to complete. Tell the children you are going to read out 20 sentences to them. Each sentence has a word missing on their answer sheet. Tell the children to listen carefully to the missing word and fill it in, making sure they spell it correctly. You will read the word, then the word within a sentence, then repeat the word a third time. Now read out each question to the children as below. At the end of the test read out all 20 sentences again.

(1) **Spelling one:** the word is **grass**.
Horses and cows eat **grass**.
The word is **grass**.

(2) **Spelling two:** the word is **watch**.
Do you **watch** much television?
The word is **watch**.

(3) **Spelling three:** the word is **dry**.
You can **dry** yourself on this towel.
The word is **dry**.

(4) **Spelling four:** the word is **magic**.
I can do **magic**.
The word is **magic**.

(5) **Spelling five:** the word is **race**.
Let's have a **race** to the end of the playground.
The word is **race**.

(6) **Spelling six:** the word is **change**.
Sammy wanted to **change** her library book.
The word is **change**.

(7) **Spelling seven:** the word is **knee**.
Ali fell over and hurt his **knee**.
The word is **knee**.

(8) **Spelling eight:** the word is **edge**.
Don't let the cup fall off the **edge** of the table.
The word is **edge**.

(9) **Spelling nine:** the word is **write**.
Please **write** your name on your books.
The word is **write**.

(10) **Spelling ten:** the word is **bottle**.
Would you like a **bottle** of juice?
The word is **bottle**.

(11) **Spelling eleven:** the word is **walked**.
Sarah **walked** to school today.
The word is **walked**.

(12) **Spelling twelve:** the word is **travel**.
I would love to **travel** to the moon and back.
The word is **travel**.

(13) **Spelling thirteen:** the word is **careful**.
You must be **careful** when using a knife.
The word is **careful**.

(14) **Spelling fourteen:** the word is **dropped**.
Alex **dropped** the glass and it broke.
The word is **dropped**.

(15) **Spelling fifteen:** the word is **station**.
The train will arrive at the **station** in ten minutes.
The word is **station**.

(16) **Spelling sixteen:** the word is **quiet**.
If you are **quiet**, you will be able to hear the birds singing.
The word is **quiet**.

(17) **Spelling seventeen:** the word is **brother**.
Victor is older than his **brother**.
The word is **brother**.

(18) **Spelling eighteen:** the word is **climb**.
It's fun to **climb** the ladder in the park.
The word is **climb**.

(19) **Spelling nineteen:** the word is **clothes**.
You are so dirty you will need to change your **clothes**.
The word is **clothes**.

(20) **Spelling twenty:** the word is **world**.
Where in the **world** would you like to visit?
The word is **world**.

Year 3   Autumn spelling test 1

> You need to add the missing words to these sentences. Your teacher will read out each missing word and then the whole sentence and will then read the missing word again. You should listen carefully and then write the word in the space. Make sure you spell each word correctly.

1 Horses and cows eat _____.

1 mark

2 Do you _____ much television?

1 mark

3 You can _____ yourself on this towel.

1 mark

4 I can do _____.

1 mark

5 Let's have a _____ to the end of the playground.

1 mark

6 Sammy wanted to _____ her library book.

1 mark

7 Ali fell over and hurt his _____.

1 mark

8 Don't let the cup fall off the _____ of the table.

1 mark

9 Please _____ your name on your books.

1 mark

10 Would you like a _____ of juice?

1 mark

/ 10

Total for this page

11) Sarah _____ to school today.

1 mark

12) I would love to _____ to the moon and back.

1 mark

13) You must be _____ when using a knife.

1 mark

14) Alex _____ the glass and it broke.

1 mark

15) The train will arrive at the _____ in ten minutes.

1 mark

16) If you are _____, you will be able to hear the birds singing.

1 mark

17) Victor is older than his _____.

1 mark

18) It's fun to _____ the ladder in the park.

1 mark

19) You are so dirty you will need to change your _____.

1 mark

20) Where in the _____ would you like to visit?

1 mark

/ 20

Total for this test

Year 3   *Autumn test 2*

Name:	Class:	Date:

1 Tick **one** box to show the noun in this sentence.

☐ ☐   ☐   ☐
↓ ↓   ↓   ↓

I like to look after animals.

☐ G
1 mark

---

2 Write the correct preposition to complete this sentence.

There is a mouse _____ my bedroom!

(in)   (over)   (up)   (at)

☐ G
1 mark

---

3 I am happy.

Circle the correct contraction for **I am**.

(Iam)   (I'm)   (Im')   (I a'm)

☐ P
1 mark

---

4 Complete this sentence.

I have long hair but Sharna's hair is _____ than mine.

☐ V
1 mark

/ 4
Total for this page

5 Add the connective that correctly completes this sentence.

Let's play inside _____ it is raining.

(and)   (but)   (because)   (or)

☐ G
1 mark

---

6 Tick the box to show where another full stop should go.

☐ ☐ ☐   ☐
↓ ↓ ↓   ↓
Cats like milk mice like cheese.

☐ P
1 mark

---

7 Tick **one** box to show the sentence that is a question.

Sit down.   ☐   What's your name?   ☐

Help!   ☐   I like ice-cream.   ☐

☐ G
1 mark

---

8 Tick the chart to show which of these words are adverbs.

Word	Adverb
jump	
quickly	
sing	
slowly	

☐ G
1 mark

/ 4
Total for this page

9 Write speech marks in the correct boxes to show what is said.

☐   ☐ ☐   ☐
↓   ↓ ↓   ↓

I had such fun, said Muhammad.

P
1 mark

---

10 Add the correct connective to complete this sentence.

Let's go out to the park _____ we finish at school.

(when)   (and)   (or)   (because)

G
1 mark

---

11 Draw lines to show which sentences can have an exclamation mark.

Where do you live

Help

Look out   !

How old are you

Stop

P
1 mark

---

12 Tick **two** words which need capital letters.

☐   ☐   ☐   ☐   ☐
↓   ↓   ↓   ↓   ↓

I am going to london on holiday with james and his family.

P
1 mark

/ 4
Total for this page

13 Add the correct prefix to the nouns to make a new word.
One has been done for you.

| mis– | dis– | sub– |

_dis_agree _____behave _____appoint

V
1 mark

---

14 Draw lines to match the nouns with the correct articles.

bun

a

egg

an

orange

roll

G
1 mark

---

15 Write commas in the correct places in this sentence.

Marius put on his jeans shirt socks and shoes.

P
1 mark

---

16 Choose the correct words to complete the sentence.
Copy the words into the spaces.

Today my favourite colour _____ blue. Yesterday it _____ yellow.

| has been | is | was | will be |

G
1 mark

/ 4
Total for this page

17 Make **two** changes and copy out the sentence correctly.

Tarik puts always his hand up to answer Questions.

_____

G
1 mark

---

18 Which of these connectives shows the **time** that Chloe went out to play?
Tick the correct sentence which shows this.

Chloe went out to play **when** she had finished her lunch. ☐

Chloe went out to play **because** she had finished all her work. ☐

Chloe went out to play **although** she felt a little ill. ☐

Chloe went out to play **and** to have her lunch. ☐

G
1 mark

---

19 joy + ful = joyful

Draw lines to show which of these words can take the suffix **-ful**.

forget

grand

help   **–ful**

hope

V
1 mark

---

20 Add the prefix that will turn these words into their opposites.

_____pleasant

_____necessary } _____

_____helpful

V
1 mark

/ 20
Total for this test

Year 3   Autumn spelling test 2: *Teacher's script*

This test should take approximately 15 minutes to complete. Tell the children you are going to read out 20 sentences to them. Each sentence has a word missing on their answer sheet. Tell the children to listen carefully to the missing word and fill it in, making sure they spell it correctly. You will read the word, then the word within a sentence, then repeat the word a third time. Now read out each question to the children as below. At the end of the test read out all 20 sentences again.

1 **Spelling one:** the word is **many**.

Many people prefer cats to dogs.

The word is **many**.

2 **Spelling two:** the word is **pencil**.

Use a **pencil** for drawing, please.

The word is **pencil**.

3 **Spelling three:** the word is **child**.

Adults say that it is lovely to be a **child**.

The word is **child**.

4 **Spelling four:** the word is **because**.

Ashley likes Thursdays **because** it is football club day.

The word is **because**.

5 **Spelling five:** the word is **hospital**.

Unfortunately Finlay's arm would need to be X-rayed at the **hospital**.

The word is **hospital**.

6 **Spelling six:** the word is **improve**.

Ethan wants to **improve** his goal scoring at football matches.

The word is **improve**.

7 **Spelling seven:** the word is **break**.

Be careful with that ball or you will **break** a window.

The word is **break**.

8 **Spelling eight:** the word is **pretty**.

What a **pretty** kitten!

The word is **pretty**.

9 **Spelling nine:** the word is **hour**.

There are sixty minutes in one **hour**.

The word is **hour**.

10 **Spelling ten:** the word is **people**.

How many **people** would like an ice-cream?

The word is **people**.

11 **Spelling eleven:** the word is **half**.

Please cut the apple in **half** to share.

The word is **half**.

12 **Spelling twelve:** the word is **should**.

All pupils **should** arrive at school on time.

The word is **should**.

(13) **Spelling thirteen:** the word is **whole**.

I could eat a **whole** pizza myself because I am so hungry.

The word is **whole**.

(14) **Spelling fourteen:** the word is **cost**.

How much money does it **cost**?

The word is **cost**.

(15) **Spelling fifteen:** the word is **usual**.

Because our teacher is absent, we do not have our **usual** lessons.

The word is **usual**.

(16) **Spelling sixteen:** the word is **hopeless**.

What a **hopeless** kick; it would never have scored a goal.

The word is **hopeless**.

(17) **Spelling seventeen:** the word is **happily**.

Kira smiled **happily** at her new puppy.

The word is **happily**.

(18) **Spelling eighteen:** the word is **everybody**.

Everybody in the class was invited to Hannah's party.

The word is **everybody**.

(19) **Spelling nineteen:** the word is **treasure**.

In stories, pirates always seem to have buried their **treasure**.

The word is **treasure**.

(20) **Spelling twenty:** the word is **mind**.

Do you **mind** if I open the window?

The word is **mind**.

Year 3 Autumn spelling test 2

You need to add the missing words to these sentences. Your teacher will read out each missing word and then the whole sentence and will then read the missing word again. You should listen carefully and then write the word in the space. Make sure you spell each word correctly.

1) _____ people prefer cats to dogs.

1 mark

2) Use a _____ for drawing, please.

1 mark

3) Adults say that it is lovely to be a _____.

1 mark

4) Ashley likes Thursdays _____ it is football club day.

1 mark

5) Unfortunately Finlay's arm would need to be X-rayed at the _____.

1 mark

6) Ethan wants to _____ his goal scoring at football matches.

1 mark

7) Be careful with that ball or you will _____ a window.

1 mark

8) What a _____ kitten!

1 mark

9) There are sixty minutes in one _____.

1 mark

10) How many _____ would like an ice-cream?

1 mark

/ 10

Total for this page

11 Please cut the apple in _____ to share.

1 mark

12 All pupils _____ arrive at school on time.

1 mark

13 I could eat a _____ pizza myself because I am so hungry.

1 mark

14 How much money does it _____?

1 mark

15 Because our teacher is absent, we do not have our

_____ lessons.

1 mark

16 What a _____ kick; it would never have scored a goal.

1 mark

17 Kira smiled _____ at her new puppy.

1 mark

18 _____ in the class was invited to Hannah's party.

1 mark

19 In stories, pirates always seem to have buried their

_____.

1 mark

20 Do you _____ if I open the window?

1 mark

/ 20

Total for this test

Year 3 *Spring test 1*

Name:	Class:	Date:

1 Write the correct word to complete this sentence.

Oh no! The dog _____ eaten my dinner.

(am)   (has)   (will)   (was)

G
1 mark

---

2 Tick the boxes to show where the speech marks should go.

☐   ☐   ☐   ☐
↓   ↓   ↓   ↓

What is your favourite colour? asked Nita.

P
1 mark

---

3 Circle the word in this sentence that is a preposition.

Jake hid the presents under his bed.

G
1 mark

---

4 Tick the chart to show which of these words are plural.

Word	Plural
mess	
pencils	
foxes	
pass	
chips	

V
1 mark

/ 4
Total for this page

5 Write a suffix to make each word into an adverb.

quick_____   bright_____

G
1 mark

---

6 Underline the correct verb.

I usually watch cartoons after school but yesterday I
watch / watched / will watch / have watched a film.

G
1 mark

---

7 Tick the boxes to show which three words should start with capital letters.

☐ ☐ ☐   ☐   ☐
↓ ↓ ↓   ↓   ↓

every sunday i go to the park with my friends.

P
1 mark

---

8 use + less = useless

Circle the words that can make a new word with the suffix **-less**.

care   fool   hope   new

V
1 mark

/ 4
Total for this page

9 Add an adjective which makes sense to this sentence.

Jamil woke up and said, "This is going to be a _____ day."

G
1 mark

---

10 Circle the connective in this sentence.

Let's have our picnic first and go for a bike ride later.

G
1 mark

---

11 Write a connective that makes sense in this sentence.

I never go swimming in the sea _____ I am afraid of the waves.

G
1 mark

---

12 Tick the boxes to show where the commas should go.

☐   ☐   ☐   ☐

We went to the zoo and saw lions tigers an elephant and a snake.

P
1 mark

G
/ 4
Total for this page

13 Draw lines to show which of these words are nouns and which are adjectives.

beautiful

goat

enormous   noun

house   adjective

tree

1 mark   G

---

14 Write out this sentence with the speech marks in the correct places.

Will you come to my party? asked Ryan.

_____

1 mark   P

---

15 Write an exclamation mark (**!**) or a question mark (**?**) to make each sentence correct.

Would you like a drink___

Oh, my goodness___

Is that a real lizard___

Ouch___

1 mark   P

---

16 Which suffix can be used to make new words from the ones below?

Write it here: _____.

dark   ill   sad

1 mark   V

/ 4

Total for this page

17 Write a question that will get the answer 'It's in my bag.'

Question:

_____

| | G |
| 1 mark | |

18 Which of these verbs could describe an action that happened yesterday?

Circle **two** words.

eat   forget   gave   helped   stand

| | G |
| 1 mark | |

19 Write '**do not**' as a contraction with an apostrophe.

I do not like vinegar on my chips.

I _____ like vinegar on my chips.

| | P |
| 1 mark | |

20 Circle the suffix that changes the word to its opposite meaning?

careful

care_____

-ly   -less   -er   -ing

| | V |
| 1 mark | |

| | / 20 |
| Total for this test | |

Year 3   Spring spelling test 1: *Teacher's script*

This test should take approximately 15 minutes to complete. Tell the children you are going to read out 20 sentences to them. Each sentence has a word missing on their answer sheet. Tell the children to listen carefully to the missing word and fill it in, making sure they spell it correctly. You will read the word, then the word within a sentence, then repeat the word a third time. Now read out each question to the children as below. At the end of the test read out all 20 sentences again.

(1) **Spelling one:** the word is **learn**.

It's fun to **learn** in our class.

The word is **learn**.

(2) **Spelling two:** the word is **forget**.

Don't **forget** your swimming kit!

The word is **forget**.

(3) **Spelling three:** the word is **garden**.

The **garden** is beautiful in the winter snow.

The word is **garden**.

(4) **Spelling four:** the word is **minute**.

I can help you in a **minute**.

The word is **minute**.

(5) **Spelling five:** the word is **circle**.

All sit in a **circle** please.

The word is **circle**.

(6) **Spelling six:** the word is **often**.

How **often** do you clean your teeth?

The word is **often**.

(7) **Spelling seven:** the word is **young**.

Even your teacher was **young** once upon a time.

The word is **young**.

(8) **Spelling eight:** the word is **eight**.

There are **eight** biscuits left in the tin.

The word is **eight**.

(9) **Spelling nine:** the word is **arrive**.

Our new puppy will **arrive** tomorrow.

The word is **arrive**.

(10) **Spelling ten:** the word is **strange**.

There is a **strange** creature outside the door.

The word is **strange**.

(11) **Spelling eleven:** the word is **decide**.

I can't **decide** whether to have chocolate or mint ice-cream.

The word is **decide**.

(12) **Spelling twelve:** the word is **appear**.

If you wait, you will see a mouse **appear** from under the cupboard.

The word is **appear**.

(13) **Spelling thirteen:** the word is **notice**.

Miss Kay put a new **notice** on the classroom door.

The word is **notice**.

(14) **Spelling fourteen:** the word is **disappoint**.

I'm sorry to **disappoint** you, but it's wet break today.

The word is **disappoint**.

(15) **Spelling fifteen:** the word is **information**.

For your **information**, school is closed at the weekend.

The word is **information**.

(16) **Spelling sixteen:** the word is **happily**.

Mr and Mrs Gorski have been **happily** married for 25 years.

The word is **happily**.

(17) **Spelling seventeen:** the word is **measure**.

To make your cake, **measure** out one cup of flour.

The word is **measure**.

(18) **Spelling eighteen:** the word is **obvious**.

It is **obvious** that you are a wonderful class.

The word is **obvious**.

(19) **Spelling nineteen:** the word is **scheme**.

Our head teacher has a new **scheme** to raise money for the school.

The word is **scheme**.

(20) **Spelling twenty:** the word is **myth**.

My favourite **myth** is the story of Icarus, who flew too close to the sun.

The word is **myth**.

Year 3   Spring spelling test 1

> You need to add the missing words to these sentences. Your teacher will read out each missing word and then the whole sentence and will then read the missing word again. You should listen carefully and then write the word in the space. Make sure you spell each word correctly.

(1)   It is fun to _____ in our class.

1 mark

(2)   Don't _____ your swimming kit!

1 mark

(3)   The _____ is beautiful in the winter snow.

1 mark

(4)   I can help you in a _____.

1 mark

(5)   All sit in a _____ please.

1 mark

(6)   How _____ do you clean your teeth?

1 mark

(7)   Even your teacher was _____ once upon a time.

1 mark

(8)   There are _____ biscuits left in the tin.

1 mark

(9)   Our new puppy will _____ tomorrow.

1 mark

(10)   There is a _____ creature outside the door.

1 mark

/ 10

Total for this page

(11) I can't _____ whether to have chocolate or mint ice-cream.

> 1 mark

(12) If you wait, you will see a mouse _____ from under the cupboard.

> 1 mark

(13) Miss Kay put a new _____ on the classroom door.

> 1 mark

(14) I'm sorry to _____ you, but it's wet break today.

> 1 mark

(15) For your _____, school is closed at the weekend.

> 1 mark

(16) Mr and Mrs Gorski have been _____ married for 25 years.

> 1 mark

(17) To make your cake, _____ out one cup of flour.

> 1 mark

(18) It is _____ that you are a wonderful class.

> 1 mark

(19) Our head teacher has a new _____ to raise money for the school.

> 1 mark

(20) My favourite _____ is the story of Icarus, who flew too close to the sun.

> 1 mark

> / 20
>
> Total for this test

Year 3   *Spring test 2*

Name:	Class:	Date:

1 Circle the word below which belongs to the same word family as '**post**'.

position   positive   possible   poster

V
1 mark

---

2 Draw lines to show which prefix belongs to each word.

dis–   appoint

mis–   marine

sub–   take

V
1 mark

---

3 Tick the sentence with the correct apostrophes.

Its Jane's cat.   ☐

It's Jane's cat.   ☐

It's Janes' cat.   ☐

I'ts Janes cat.   ☐

P
1 mark

---

4 Write the correct connectives in this sentence.

Owen is fond of rice _____ he likes potatoes _____ he doesn't like pasta.

and   but   if   or

G
1 mark

/ 4
Total for this page

5 Circle the **two** prepositions in this sentence.

Before I get into bed, I put my reading book on my pillow.

G
1 mark

---

6 Write the correct punctuation into the boxes above these sentences.
Use **!** or **?**

☐   ☐   ☐

Have you heard It's Eva's birthday Do you think there will be a party

P
1 mark

---

7 Circle the connective in this sentence.

Viktor has to go straight to bed when he gets home.

G
1 mark

---

8 Tick the chart to show which of these words are nouns.

Word	Noun
think	
open	
classroom	
lunchtime	
playing	

G
1 mark

/ 4
Total for this page

9 Write a punctuation mark to complete this sentence.

Have you ever seen a full moon___

P
1 mark

---

10 Tick the correct way to complete this sentence.

Felix used to live in France but he _____ next to me for two years now.

lived ☐   used to live ☐

has lived ☐   had lived ☐

G
1 mark

---

11 Add **one** word to complete this sentence.

Mr Jones is my favourite teacher because _____ knows lots of jokes.

G
1 mark

---

12 Write the **one** word that is missing from **both** of these sentences.

Please sit on [   ] left.

I love going to [   ] park.

V
1 mark

/ 4
Total for this page

13 Add **two** adjectives which make sense to this sentence.

> Look at that _____ _____ elephant!

G
1 mark

---

14 Circle the connective to complete this sentence.

Navaeh stood on a bench _____ she could see over the wall.

because   when   if   so

G
1 mark

---

15 Write the correct adverbs in these instructions.

_____ put the eggs into a bowl.

_____ add flour and milk and beat together for a pancake mixture.

After   Before   First   Next

G
1 mark

---

16 Rewrite this sentence using commas in the correct places.

Have you got any red blue green or yellow marbles?

_____

P
1 mark

/ 4
Total for this page

17 Draw lines to match the prefixes with the correct words.

super–   pilot

auto–   human

anti–   clockwise

1 mark   V

---

18 Why are speech marks used in this sentence?

"Try to catch the ball," called Anna.

Speech marks are used because _____

_____

1 mark   P

---

19 Write **one** word in each gap to complete the sentence.

For my last holiday I _____ to visit my aunt. For my next holiday

I _____ visit my uncle.

want   went   will   wish

1 mark   G

---

20 Explain why capital letters have been used for two words in this sentence.

Can we take James to the seaside with us?

C for Can: _____

J for James: _____

1 mark   P

/ 20

Total for this test

Year 3   Spring spelling test 2: *Teacher's script*

This test should take approximately 15 minutes to complete. Tell the children you are going to read out 20 sentences to them. Each sentence has a word missing on their answer sheet. Tell the children to listen carefully to the missing word and fill it in, making sure they spell it correctly. You will read the word, then the word within a sentence, then repeat the word a third time. Now read out each question to the children as below. At the end of the test read out all 20 sentences again.

(1) **Spelling one:** the word is **group**.

Sajad and Joe are in the same **group** for cooking lessons.

The word is **group**.

(2) **Spelling two:** the word is **busy**.

Izabela is always **busy** reading her book.

The word is **busy**.

(3) **Spelling three:** the word is **difficult**.

That sum was very **difficult** but I did it!

The word is **difficult**.

(4) **Spelling four:** the word is **describe**.

It is hard to **describe** the snake I saw because it moved so fast.

The word is **describe**.

(5) **Spelling five:** the word is **grammar**.

I am good at **grammar** questions now.

The word is **grammar**.

(6) **Spelling six:** the word is **disappear**.

The magician made the rabbit **disappear**.

The word is **disappear**.

(7) **Spelling seven:** the word is **February**.

My birthday is in **February**.

The word is **February**.

(8) **Spelling eight:** the word is **special**.

This is my **special** pen.

The word is **special**.

(9) **Spelling nine:** the word is **tongue**.

Please do not stick out your **tongue** in class!

The word is **tongue**.

(10) **Spelling ten:** the word is **accept**.

I will **accept** your apology. Thank you.

The word is **accept**.

(11) **Spelling eleven:** the word is **answer**.

That's a brilliant **answer**!

The word is **answer**.

(12) **Spelling twelve:** the word is **fruit**.

Strawberries are my favourite **fruit**.

The word is **fruit.**

(13) **Spelling thirteen:** the word is **completely**.

Yes. You are **completely** right. That is the correct answer.

The word is **completely.**

(14) **Spelling fourteen:** the word is **simply**.

If you can't see in the dark, **simply** switch on a torch.

The word is **simply**.

(15) **Spelling fifteen:** the word is **impossible**.

Nothing is **impossible** if you believe you can do it.

The word is **impossible**.

(16) **Spelling sixteen:** the word is **treasure**.

Pirates are always looking for buried **treasure**.

The word is **treasure**.

(17) **Spelling seventeen:** the word is **beginning**.

Let's start at the **beginning**.

The word is **beginning**.

(18) **Spelling eighteen:** the word is **machine**.

Switch off the **machine** when you have finished with it.

The word is **machine**.

(19) **Spelling nineteen:** the word is **mystery**.

I love a story that's full of **mystery**.

The word is **mystery**.

(20) **Spelling twenty:** the word is **vein**.

Can you see the **vein** in your wrist?

The word is **vein**.

Year 3   Spring spelling test 2

You need to add the missing words to these sentences. Your teacher will read out each missing word and then the whole sentence and will then read the missing word again. You should listen carefully and then write the word in the space. Make sure you spell each word correctly.

1. Sajad and Joe are in the same _____ for cooking lessons.

   1 mark

2. Izabela is always _____ reading her book.

   1 mark

3. That sum was very _____ but I did it!

   1 mark

4. It is hard to _____ the snake I saw because it moved so fast.

   1 mark

5. I am good at _____ questions now.

   1 mark

6. The magician made the rabbit _____.

   1 mark

7. My birthday is in _____.

   1 mark

8. This is my _____ pen.

   1 mark

9. Please do not stick out your _____ in class!

   1 mark

10. I will _____ your apology. Thank you.

   1 mark

/ 10

Total for this page

(11) That's a brilliant _____!

1 mark

(12) Strawberries are my favourite _____.

1 mark

(13) Yes. You are _____ right. That is the correct
answer.

1 mark

(14) If you can't see in the dark, _____ switch on a torch.

1 mark

(15) Nothing is _____ if you believe you can do it.

1 mark

(16) Pirates are always looking for buried _____.

1 mark

(17) Let's start at the _____.

1 mark

(18) Switch off the _____ when you have finished
with it.

1 mark

(19) I love a story that's full of _____.

1 mark

(20) Can you see the _____ in your wrist?

1 mark

/ 20
Total for this test

Year 3   *Summer test 1*

Name:	Class:	Date:

1 Tick the boxes above the words that should begin with a capital letter.

☐ ↓   ☐ ↓   ☐ ↓   ☐ ↓

ben was looking forward to visiting australia with his family.

P
1 mark

---

2 Write **two** adjectives to give more information about the noun.

Erin loved her _____ _____ brother very much.

G
1 mark

---

3 Circle the prefix which turns the word into its opposite meaning.

social

anti–	super–	auto–	pre–

V
1 mark

---

4 Write the commas in the correct places in this sentence.

I enjoy learning about the people places food and sports of other countries.

P
1 mark

/ 4
Total for this page

5 Circle the correct time connective to complete this sentence.

It is good to clean your teeth _____ you go to bed.

after   and   before   next

G
1 mark

---

6 Put a tick in the correct column to show whether the sentence is a question or a command.

Sentence	Question	Command
How are you		
Open the window		
Will you feed the cat please		

G
1 mark

---

7 Tick the box to show the correct preposition to complete this sentence.

I keep my favourite books in a box _____ my bed.

at ☐   between ☐   in ☐   under ☐

G
1 mark

---

8 Tick the pair of words with the correct use of apostrophes.

can't   do'not   ☐

can't   don't   ☐

ca'nt   d'ont   ☐

cant   don't   ☐

P
1 mark

/ 4
Total for this page

9 Write a verb that makes sense to this sentence.

Last week, school _____ early because it was snowing hard.

G
1 mark

---

10 Underline the subordinating connective in this sentence.

Rabbits can be scared if they hear loud noises.

G
1 mark

---

11 Tick the sentences which should have a question mark.

Can you swim ☐

Sofia is a fast runner ☐

Watch out ☐

When are we going ☐

P
1 mark

---

12 Circle the correct word or words to complete this sentence.

I _____ at school for three years now.

| am | have been | was | will | be |

G
1 mark

/ 4
Total for this page

13 Add an adjective to this sentence.

Cats are _____ animals.

G
1 mark

---

14 Draw lines from 'a' and 'an' to show which words they go with.

ant

a

bear

an

elephant

horse

V
1 mark

---

15 Circle the word that is not correct in this sentence.

In my dream, I were chased by three monsters.

G
1 mark

---

16 Draw a line to link the **two** opposite adverbs.

sadly   walk

quickly   happily

jump   smile

G
1 mark

/ 4
Total for this page

17 Write the root word for this word family.

agreeable   agreement   disagree   disagreeable

_____

1 mark V

---

18 Rewrite this sentence adding a comma in a suitable place.

When it's raining I love to jump in the puddles.

_____

1 mark P

---

19 Tick the boxes to show which of these adjectives can become nouns by adding the suffix **-ness**.

beautiful ☐   careful ☐   slow ☐   thoughtful ☐

1 mark V

---

20 Rewrite this sentence adding the correct speech marks.

This is my best birthday ever, said Ali.

_____

1 mark P

/ 20

Total for this test

Year 3   Summer spelling test 1: *Teacher's script*

This test should take approximately 15 minutes to complete. Tell the children you are going to read out 20 sentences to them. Each sentence has a word missing on their answer sheet. Tell the children to listen carefully to the missing word and fill it in, making sure they spell it correctly. You will read the word, then the word within a sentence, then repeat the word a third time. Now read out each question to the children as below. At the end of the test read out all 20 sentences again.

(1) **Spelling one:** the word is **woman**.

The **woman** on the left is my aunt.

The word is **woman**.

(2) **Spelling two:** the word is **remember**.

I can never **remember** jokes.

The word is **remember**.

(3) **Spelling three:** the word is **prefer**.

Would you **prefer** an apple or an orange?

The word is **prefer**.

(4) **Spelling four:** the word is **believe**.

Do you **believe** in ghosts?

The word is **believe**.

(5) **Spelling five:** the word is **heard**.

I **heard** that there will be free pizza at lunchtime.

The word is **heard**.

(6) **Spelling six:** the word is **bicycle**.

I'm getting a new **bicycle** for my birthday.

The word is **bicycle**.

(7) **Spelling seven:** the word is **eight**.

Spiders have **eight** legs.

The word is **eight**.

(8) **Spelling eight:** the word is **groan**.

There was a **groan** when the comedian told the same old joke again.

The word is **groan**.

(9) **Spelling nine:** the word is **address**.

What is the school **address**?

The word is **address**.

(10) **Spelling ten:** the word is **accident**.

Isaac broke the window by **accident**.

The word is **accident**.

(11) **Spelling eleven:** the word is **opposite**.

I live **opposite** the park.

The word is **opposite**.

(12) **Spelling twelve:** the word is **regular**.

It is important to have a **regular** check-up with your dentist.

The word is **regular**.

(13) **Spelling thirteen:** the word is **calendar**.

Each year I buy a new **calendar** to put birthdays on.

The word is **calendar**.

(14) **Spelling fourteen:** the word is **scene**.

My favourite **scene** in the film was when the animals started to speak.

The word is **scene**.

(15) **Spelling fifteen:** the word is **enormous**.

What an **enormous** ice-cream!

The word is **enormous**.

(16) **Spelling sixteen:** the word is **injection**.

Having an **injection** is not as bad as you think.

The word is **injection**.

(17) **Spelling seventeen:** the word is **gardener**.

The park **gardener** does a wonderful job.

The word is **gardener**.

(18) **Spelling eighteen:** the word is **trouble**.

I knew that dog would be **trouble**.

The word is **trouble**.

(19) **Spelling nineteen:** the word is **pleasure**.

It is my **pleasure** to welcome you to this class.

The word is **pleasure**.

(20) **Spelling twenty:** the word is **disobey**.

Why did you **disobey** my instructions?

The word is **disobey**.

Year 3   Summer spelling test 1

You need to add the missing words to these sentences. Your teacher will read out each missing word and then the whole sentence and will then read the missing word again. You should listen carefully and then write the word in the space. Make sure you spell each word correctly.

1 The _____ on the left is my aunt.

1 mark

2 I can never _____ jokes.

1 mark

3 Would you _____ an apple or an orange?

1 mark

4 Do you _____ in ghosts?

1 mark

5 I _____ that there will be free pizza at lunchtime.

1 mark

6 I'm getting a new _____ for my birthday.

1 mark

7 Spiders have _____ legs.

1 mark

8 There was a _____ when the comedian told the same old joke again.

1 mark

9 What is the school _____?

1 mark

10 Isaac broke the window by _____.

1 mark

/ 10

Total for this page

11   I live _____ the park.

12   It is important to have a _____ check-up with your dentist.

13   Each year I buy a new _____ to put birthdays on.

14   My favourite _____ in the film was when the animals started to speak.

15   What an _____ ice-cream!

16   Having an _____ is not as bad as you think.

17   The park _____ does a wonderful job.

18   I knew that dog would be _____.

19   It is my _____ to welcome you to this class.

20   Why did you _____ my instructions?

Year 3   *Summer test 2*

Name:	Class:	Date:

1 Circle the word that can make a new word by adding **-ful**.

care   happy   quick   sad

V
1 mark

---

2 Tick the correct contraction of '**did not**'.

did'nt ☐

didn't ☐

di'dnt ☐

d'idnt ☐

P
1 mark

---

3 Tick the box to show the adverb in this sentence.

☐   ☐   ☐   ☐
↓   ↓   ↓   ↓
Luca quickly climbed into bed to read his favourite book.

G
1 mark

---

4 Write the correct connective to this sentence.

Toma loves to paddle in the sea _____ she doesn't like to swim.

and   but   or   so

G
1 mark

/ 4

Total for this page

54

5 Tick the box to show where the missing full stop should go.

☐ ☐   ☐ ☐
↓ ↓   ↓ ↓

Jenna likes to play with Sam Gina likes to play with Agna.

P
1 mark

---

6 Write the correct connective in this sentence.

We could go to the zoo today _____ you would like to see the animals.

(although)   (if)   (when)   (while)

G
1 mark

---

7 Write the correct verb form in this sentence.

Liam _____ to Finland for his holiday last year.

(has been)   (go)   (going)   (went)

G
1 mark

---

8 Circle the **two** nouns in this sentence.

I've looked under the bed and in the cupboard and I still can't find it.

G
1 mark

/ 4
Total for this page

9 Tick the box to show which one of these sentences contains an exclamation mark.

What are you doing? ☐

It's coming ... ☐

Help! ☐

I ate lots of ice-cream. ☐

P
1 mark

---

10 Add the correct connective to this sentence.

I would love to come out to play _____ I've finished my dinner.

G
1 mark

---

11 Add **two** adjectives to this sentence to give more information.

Jo has a _____ _____ coat.

G
1 mark

---

12 Tick the chart to show which words are adverbs.

Word	Adverb
angrily	
cleverly	
simply	
truthful	

G
1 mark

/ 4
Total for this page

13 Add the correct words to the sentence below.

Mr Andrews and Miss Chan have worked at this school for one year but

Mrs Adler _____ here for 20 years.

G

1 mark

14 Rewrite this sentence using correct capital letters.

On saturday, mr benitez is going to london with his son, jonas.

_____

P

1 mark

15 Write the correct pronoun in the sentence.

Hameed enjoys playing cricket and _____ is very good at catching and throwing.

G

1 mark

16 Why are commas used in this sentence?

We bought milk, bread, tomatoes and cheese.

_____

P

1 mark

/ 4

Total for this page

17 Which prefix can be added to all of these words to change the meanings to their opposites?

happy   believable   tidy

_____

V
1 mark

---

18 Add the correct word ('a' or 'an') before these nouns.

_____ antelope

_____ buffalo

_____ giraffe

_____ ostrich

V
1 mark

---

19 Rewrite this sentence using correct speech marks.

Hurry up, said Lucy.

_____

P
1 mark

---

20 What is the root word for this group of words?

poster postman postbox

_____

V
1 mark

/ 20
Total for this test

Year 3   Summer spelling test 2: *Teacher's script*

This test should take approximately 15 minutes to complete. Tell the children you are going to read out 20 sentences to them. Each sentence has a word missing on their answer sheet. Tell the children to listen carefully to the missing word and fill it in, making sure they spell it correctly. You will read the word, then the word within a sentence, then repeat the word a third time. Now read out each question to the children as below. At the end of the test read out all 20 sentences again.

1 **Spelling one:** the word is **interest**.

Jorge showed great **interest** in the new computer.

The word is **interest**.

2 **Spelling two:** the word is **probably**.

Our team will **probably** win the match.

The word is **probably**.

3 **Spelling three:** the word is **business**.

My neighbour works for a garage **business**.

The word is **business**.

4 **Spelling four:** the word is **enough**.

Have you had **enough** to eat?

The word is **enough**.

5 **Spelling five:** the word is **favourite**.

My **favourite** colour is green.

The word is **favourite**.

6 **Spelling six:** the word is **promise**.

I **promise** that I'll be your best friend.

The word is **promise**.

7 **Spelling seven:** the word is **possible**.

I didn't think it was **possible** to eat that many bananas!

The word is **possible**.

8 **Spelling eight:** the word is **certain**.

Mr Grey is **certain** that it will be sunny for sports day.

The word is **certain**.

9 **Spelling nine:** the word is **particular**.

Do you have any **particular** dislikes?

The word is **particular**.

10 **Spelling ten:** the word is **peace**.

I can find **peace** and quiet at the end of my garden.

The word is **peace**.

11 **Spelling eleven:** the word is **angrily**.

Matthew stomped **angrily** down the stairs.

The word is **angrily**.

12 **Spelling twelve:** the word is **suppose**.

Do you **suppose** we will be able to bring our cameras on the school trip?

The word is **suppose**.

(13) **Spelling thirteen:** the word is **supermarket**.

We go to the **supermarket** at the weekend.

The word is **supermarket**.

(14) **Spelling fourteen:** the word is **presentation**.

Please try to improve your **presentation**.

The word is **presentation**.

(15) **Spelling fifteen:** the word is **double**.

Sam works at **double** the speed of Mark.

The word is **double**.

(16) **Spelling sixteen:** the word is **refresh**.

On a hot day, splash water on your face to **refresh** yourself.

The word is **refresh**.

(17) **Spelling seventeen:** the word is **unique**.

You are all **unique** individuals.

The word is **unique**.

(18) **Spelling eighteen:** the word is **expression**.

When you eat something very cold, your face makes a strange **expression**.

The word is **expression**.

(19) **Spelling nineteen:** the word is **chemist**.

You can ask the **chemist** for some medicines instead of the doctor.

The word is **chemist**.

(20) **Spelling twenty:** the word is **neighbour**.

My **neighbour** is extremely kind.

The word is **neighbour**.

Year 3   Summer spelling test 2

You need to add the missing words to these sentences. Your teacher will read out each missing word and then the whole sentence and will then read the missing word again. You should listen carefully and then write the word in the space. Make sure you spell each word correctly.

1 Jorge showed great _____ in the new computer.

2 Our team will _____ win the match.

3 My neighbour works for a garage _____.

4 Have you had _____ to eat?

5 My _____ colour is green.

6 I _____ that I'll be your best friend.

7 I didn't think it was _____ to eat that many bananas!

8 Mr Grey is _____ that it will be sunny for sports day.

9 Do you have any _____ dislikes?

10 I can find _____ and quiet at the end of my garden.

1 mark

1 mark

1 mark

1 mark

1 mark

1 mark

1 mark

1 mark

1 mark

1 mark

/ 10

Total for this page

(11) Matthew stomped _____ down the stairs.

1 mark

(12) Do you _____ we will be able to bring our cameras on the school trip?

1 mark

(13) We go to the _____ at the weekend.

1 mark

(14) Please try to improve your _____.

1 mark

(15) Sam works at _____ the speed of Mark.

1 mark

(16) On a hot day, splash water on your face to _____ yourself.

1 mark

(17) You are all _____ individuals.

1 mark

(18) When you eat something very cold, your face makes a strange _____.

1 mark

(19) You can ask the _____ for some medicines instead of the doctor.

1 mark

(20) My _____ is extremely kind.

1 mark

/ 20

Total for this test

Answers and mark schemes

Autumn test 1

	Answer	Area	Mark	Extra information
1	and	G	1	
2	☑ ☐ ☐☐ please bring your swimming kit tomorrow.	P	1	
3	Go to bed.	G	1	
4	peaches, bananas	V	1	Award 1 mark for both correct.
5	dark, sad	V	1	Award 1 mark for both correct.
6	☐ ☑ ☐ ☐ I know that ben likes tennis.	P	1	
7	because	G	1	
8	looked	G	1	
9	but	G	1	
10	☐ ☑ ☑ ☐ Sanji's favourite animals are lions tigers bears and elephants.	P	1	Award 1 mark for both correct.
11	a — ant / flower / insect / tree an (lines crossing)	V	1	Award 1 mark for all correct.
12	☑ ☑ ☐ ☐ You are my best friend, said Noor.	P	1	Award 1 mark for both correct.
13	if *or* when	G	1	
14	Accept any suitable adjective, e.g. new, blue, big.	G	1	Do not accept a number, e.g. two.
15	Accept any suitable question.	G	1	Spelling is not assessed but grammar should be correct.
16	faster	G	1	
17	-ful	V	1	
18	I like making bread on Saturdays.	G	1	
19	Apostrophes are used in these words because letters are missing/ they replace letters.	P	1	Do not accept 'to make sense'.
20	! is used because/to show it is said loudly or the speaker is surprised/shocked.	P	1	

Autumn test 2

	Answer	Area	Mark	Extra information
1	☐ ☐ ☐ ✓ ↓ ↓ ↓ ↓ I like to look after animals.	G	1	
2	in	G	1	
3	I'm	P	1	
4	Accept any suitable comparative adjective, e.g. longer/curlier/browner.	V	1	
5	because	G	1	
6	☐ ☐ ✓ ☐ ↓ ↓ ↓ ↓ Cats like milk mice like cheese.	P	1	
7	What's your name?	G	1	
8	<table><tr><td>Word</td><td>Adverb</td></tr><tr><td>jump</td><td></td></tr><tr><td>quickly</td><td>✓</td></tr><tr><td>sing</td><td></td></tr><tr><td>slowly</td><td>✓</td></tr></table>	G	1	Award 1 mark for both adverbs correct.
9	✓ ✓ ☐ ☐ ↓ ↓ ↓ ↓ I had such fun, said Muhammad.	P	1	Award 1 mark for both correct.
10	when	G	1	
11	Where do you live Help ⎯ Look out ⎯⎯⎯⎯⎯⎯ ! How old are you Stop ⎯	P	1	Award 1 mark for both correct.
12	☐ ✓ ☐ ✓ ☐ ↓ ↓ ↓ ↓ ↓ I am going to london on holiday with james and his family.	P	1	Award 1 mark for both correct.
13	misbehave, disappoint	V	1	Award 1 mark for both correct.
14	a ⎯ bun / egg / orange / roll an ⎯	G	1	Award 1 mark for all correct.
15	Marius put on his jeans, shirt, socks and shoes.	P	1	Award 1 mark for both correct.
16	Today my favourite colour **is** blue. Yesterday it **was** yellow.	G	1	Award 1 mark for both correct.
17	Tarik always puts his hand up to answer questions.	G	1	Award 1 mark for both correct.
18	Chloe went out to play **when** she had finished her lunch.	G	1	
19	forget, help, hope	V	1	Award 1 mark for all correct.
20	un–	V	1	

Spring test 1

	Answer	Area	Mark	Extra information
1	has	G	1	
2	☑ ☑ ☐ ☐ What is your favourite colour? asked Nita.	P	1	Award 1 mark for both correct.
3	under	G	1	
4	<table><tr><td>**Word**</td><td>**Plural**</td></tr><tr><td>mess</td><td></td></tr><tr><td>pencils</td><td>✓</td></tr><tr><td>foxes</td><td>✓</td></tr><tr><td>pass</td><td></td></tr><tr><td>chips</td><td>✓</td></tr></table>	V	1	Award 1 mark for all correct.
5	quickly, brightly	G	1	Award 1 mark for both correct.
6	watched	G	1	
7	☑ ☑ ☑ ☐ ☐ every sunday i go to the park with my friends.	P	1	Award 1 mark for all correct.
8	care, hope	V	1	Award 1 mark for both correct.
9	Accept any suitable adjective, e.g. lovely, fine, busy, awful.	G	1	
10	and	G	1	
11	because *or* as	G	1	Do not accept 'and'.
12	☐ ☑ ☑ ☐ We went to the zoo and saw lions tigers an elephant and a snake.	P	1	Award 1 mark for both correct.
13	beautiful — adjective goat — noun enormous — adjective house — noun tree — noun	G	1	Award 1 mark for all correct.
14	"Will you come to my party?" asked Ryan.	P	1	
15	Would you like a drink? Oh, my goodness! Is that a real lizard? Ouch!	P	1	Award 1 mark for all correct.
16	-ness	V	1	Accept answers where the suffix has been added to the given words.
17	Accept any suitable question.	G	1	The question mark must be included.
18	gave, helped	G	1	Award 1 mark for both correct.
19	don't	P	1	
20	-less	V	1	

Spring test 2

	Answer	Area	Mark	Extra information
1	poster	V	1	
2	dis- ——————— appoint mis- ——— marine sub- ——— take	V	1	Award 1 mark for all correct.
3	It's Jane's cat.	P	1	
4	Owen is fond of rice **and** he likes potatoes **but** he doesn't like pasta.	G	1	Award 1 mark for both correct.
5	into, on	G	1	Award 1 mark for both correct.
6	[?] [!] [?] Have you heard It's Eva's birthday Do you think there will be a party	P	1	Award 1 mark for all correct.
7	when	G	1	
8	<table><tr><td>Word</td><td>Noun</td></tr><tr><td>think</td><td></td></tr><tr><td>open</td><td></td></tr><tr><td>classroom</td><td>✓</td></tr><tr><td>lunchtime</td><td>✓</td></tr><tr><td>playing</td><td></td></tr></table>	G	1	Award 1 mark for both nouns correct.
9	Have you ever seen a full moon?	P	1	
10	has lived	G	1	
11	he	G	1	
12	the	V	1	
13	Accept any two suitable adjectives, e.g. enormous, grey, friendly.	G	1	Conventional word order of adjectives is not part of the assessment for this item.
14	so	G	1	
15	**First** put the eggs into a bowl. **Next** add flour and milk and beat together for a pancake mixture.	G	1	Award 1 mark for both correct.
16	Have you got any red, blue, green or yellow marbles?	P	1	Award 1 mark for all correct.
17	super- ——— pilot auto- ——— human anti- ——————— clockwise	V	1	Award 1 mark for all correct.
18	Speech marks are used because they indicate what the speaker has actually said/they show what she said/they are what is spoken out loud.	P	1	Do not accept: they show who is speaking.
19	For my last holiday I **went** to visit my aunt. For my next holiday I **will** visit my uncle.	G	1	Award 1 mark for both correct.
20	C for Can: it begins a sentence. J for James: for a person's name/proper noun.	P	1	Award 1 mark for both correct.

Summer test 1

	Answer	Area	Mark	Extra information
1	☑ ☐ ☑ ☐ ⬇ ⬇ ⬇ ⬇ ben was looking forward to visiting australia with his family	P	1	Award 1 mark for both correct.
2	Accept any relevant adjectives, e.g. good, little, naughty, younger.	G	1	The comma is not required to gain the mark.
3	anti-	V	1	
4	I enjoy learning about the people, places, food and sports of other countries.	P	1	Award 1 mark for both correct.
5	before	G	1	
6	How are you? Question Open the window. Command Will you feed the cat please? Question	G	1	Award 1 mark for all correct.
7	under	G	1	
8	can't, don't	P	1	
9	Accept any appropriate answer in the past tense, e.g. started, finished, ended, etc.	G	1	
10	if	G	1	
11	Can you swim? When are we going?	P	1	Award 1 mark for both correct.
12	have been	G	1	
13	Accept any appropriate adjective, e.g. friendly, clean.	G	1	
14	a — ant — bear an — elephant — horse (a→elephant/horse, an→ant/bear crossed)	V	1	Award 1 mark for all correct.
15	were	G	1	
16	sadly–happily	G	1	
17	agree	V	1	
18	When it's raining, I love to jump in the puddles.	P	1	
19	careful, slow, thoughtful	V	1	Award 1 mark for all correct.
20	"This is my best birthday ever," said Ali.	P	1	Award 1 mark for both correct.

Summer test 2

	Answer	Area	Mark	Extra information
1	care	V	1	
2	didn't	P	1	
3	☑ ☐ ☐ ☐ Luca quickly climbed into bed to read his favourite book.	G	1	
4	but	G	1	
5	☐ ☐ ☑ ☐ Jenna likes to play with Sam Gina likes to play with Agna.	P	1	
6	if	G	1	
7	went	G	1	
8	bed, cupboard	G	1	Award 1 mark for both correct.
9	Help!	P	1	
10	Accept any suitable time connective, e.g. after, when.	G	1	
11	Accept any relevant adjectives, e.g. warm, new, red, furry, bright.	G	1	Award 1 mark for both correct.
12	<table><tr><th>Word</th><th>Adverb</th></tr><tr><td>angrily</td><td>✓</td></tr><tr><td>cleverly</td><td>✓</td></tr><tr><td>simply</td><td>✓</td></tr><tr><td>truthful</td><td></td></tr></table>	G	1	Award 1 mark for all, with no incorrect entries.
13	has worked *or* has been	G	1	
14	On Saturday, Mr Benitez is going to London with his son, Jonas.	P	1	Award 1 mark for all five correct capitals.
15	Hameed enjoys playing cricket and **he** is very good at catching and throwing.	G	1	The capital letter is not required for the mark.
16	Accept any answers that refer to a list.	P	1	
17	un–	V	1	
18	an antelope a buffalo a giraffe an ostrich	V	1	Award 1 mark for all correct.
19	"Hurry up," said Lucy.	P	1	
20	post	V	1	